SKATE JOURNAL
CONTENTS PAGE

D1590897

DISCLAIMER

Despite the substantial amount of efforts directed towards maintaining the accuracy of information throughout the book, the author and publisher do not assume and responsibility and thereby deny liability for any loss, damage, or disruption caused due to errors or omissions to any party, regardless of the cause of the emergence of such errors or omissions.

This book is not a substitute for professional medical advice, diagnosis or treatment and we urge readers to consult a physician in matters relating to their health, particularly when any symptoms require diagnosis or medical attention. Similar to any other sport involving speed, balance and external factors, skating poses some inherent risk. The readers must take full responsibility for their safety and ensure that their equipment is properly maintained. Do not push yourselves beyond your limits.

The writer of this book makes no warranties or representations, express or implied, as to the accuracy, completeness, timeliness or usefulness of any of the information incorporated in this book. The writer reserves the right to alter information within this book at any time. By using this book, you agree that the writer or any other party involved in creating or delivering this or related content will not be liable to you in any manner, for any decision, action or nonaction undertaken by you based on your interpretation of the content.

Although we strive to provide links to useful and ethical websites, we do not possess control over the content of these sites and the links to such sites do not act as an endorsement for all their content.

Disclosure: You should assume that the writer of this book is an affiliate for prov iders of goods and services mentioned in this book. The owner

SKATE JOURNAL

ABOUT ME

This Journal Belongs to

_____

I started skating when i was _____ years old

My Favorite Thing about Skating is:

My Favorite Tricks are:

My Most challenging Tricks are:

My Skating Goals:

SKATE JOURNAL

BEST SKILLS

STREET

PARK

TRANSITION

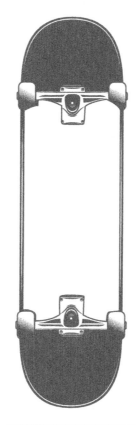

HABIT TRACKER

Month _____   Year _____

Day															
1															
2															
3															
4															
5															
6															
7															
8															
9															
10															
11															
12															
13															
14															
15															
16															
17															
18															
19															
20															
21															
22															
23															
24															
25															
26															
27															
28															
29															
30															
31															

Weekly Planner

week of _____

MONDAY

TUESDAY

WEDNESDAY

THURSDAY

FRIDAY

SATURDAY

SUNDAY

◎ GOALS

_____

_____

_____

_____

_____

_____

_____

FEELINGS, SUMMARY, PROGRESS

WEEKLY QUOTES

Remember: Support your local skate shop!

PARTS OF A SKATEBOARD

Griptape

Bolts

Wheels

Trucks

Bearings
(inside wheels
not visible)

POTENTIAL OBSTACLES

Skateboarding has many types of obstacles that come in all shapes and sizes.

Each obstacle presents its own unique challenge and offers its own type of fun.

Here are some basic obstacles that can be found in your local skate park or city scape

CURB	PARKING BLOCK	PARK BENCH	PICNIC TABLE	WALL
GAP	CONE	TRASH CAN	STAIRS	POLE JAM
HANDRAIL	MANUAL PAD	BOWL	MINI RAMP	QUARTER RIPE
HALF PIPE	BANK	LOOP	AFRAME	PYRAMID
	EURO GAP	HIP		

Weekly Planner

week of _____

MONDAY

TUESDAY

WEDNESDAY

THURSDAY

FRIDAY

SATURDAY

SUNDAY

🎯 GOALS

_____

_____

_____

_____

_____

_____

WEEKLY QUOTES

❝

I consider skateboarding an art
form, a lifestyle and a sport

❞

Tony Hawk

STANCE

When you are on your board, and you haven't started moving around, it is crucial to get used to your stance.

1. Position your feet across the board, and point your toes in a forward direction.

2. Once on the board, ensure that the weight is placed equally on both feet and they are placed shoulder-width apart.

3. Stand on top of the bolts in a way that you are parallel to the deck's center-line.

While skateboarding, you can undertake one of the two stances: goofy or regular.

Goofy: If an individual chooses to ride goofy it means that they skate by placing their right foot forward and that they use their left foot to push the board.

Regular: If an individual chooses to ride regular it means that they skate by placing their left foot forward and use their right foot to push the board.

Your stance could also include Nollie, Fakie, Switch.

PUSHING

As the name suggests, "pushing" enables the rider to move. These are the steps one must follow to start pushing:

1. Position your front foot behind the front truck on top of the board.

2. Place your other foot on the ground, adjacent to the board's center.

3. In a smooth manner, start by kicking the foot placed on the ground in the backward direction.

4. At the end of the kick, remember to twist your other foot, ensuring that it stays across the board.

5. Allow the rear foot to sit on the board now and maintain your stance. It is important to ensure that the weight placed on both feet on top of the board is equal.

Weekly Planner

week of _____

MONDAY

TUESDAY

WEDNESDAY

THURSDAY

FRIDAY

SATURDAY

SUNDAY

🎯 GOALS

_____

_____

_____

_____

_____

_____

_____

FEELINGS, SUMMARY, PROGRESS

WEEKLY QUOTES

The Board or Deck is the part
of the board that we stand
on. We generally refer to the
whole skateboard set up as
"the board" and the deck is just
the board by itself.

Note: Pushing mongo is pushing with your front foot instead of your back foot. While your back foot is over the back truck your front foot is used to push.

Note: Pushing mongoincreaees difficulty and instabily when you increase speed. This is why some people frown upon it.

FAKIE

Skating Fakie is when your feet are in the position of your normal stance and you are rolling opposite the direction that you would be rolling normally

So when a regular footed person skates Fakie, their right foot is in front and they use the right foot to pop their tricks.

Likewise when a goofy footed person skates Fakie, they have their left foot in front and pop their tricks with their left foot.

NOTE: Rolling fakie looks like rolling switch stance except we pop tricks off of the leading part of our board

SWITCH

Skating switch means to skate in the stance that is not your normal stance

For example, if the regular footed stance is your normal stance then when you skate with the goofy footed stance you are skating Switch.

Like wise when your normal stance is the goofy footed stance
Whenever you skate regular footed then you are skating switch stance.

Note: remember to have fun with skating and try not to get too distracted by the "rules" or status quo's.

If it's fun for you and it's not harming any one then go for it.

Weekly Planner

week of _____

MONDAY

TUESDAY

WEDNESDAY

THURSDAY

FRIDAY

SATURDAY

SUNDAY

◎ GOALS

_____
_____
_____
_____
_____
_____
_____

FEELINGS, SUMMARY, PROGRESS

WEEKLY QUOTES

Proper Gnar is the first black-woman owned skateboard company offering unique designs for their decks, apparel, and art.

TIC TAC

The Tic Tac is very fundamental In that it is a way to propel ourselves or even change our direction.

Tic Tacs are preformed by lifting the front of your board off of the ground then turning about 45 degrees either frontside or backside and placing the board back down.

Then turn in the other direction and repeat these steps to propel yourself forward.

Keep a steady pace and enjoy your new move.

TIP: looking forward will help you steer the board while you Tic Tac

NOTE: the Tic Tac gets its name from the sound that your wheels make when they hit the Ground.

CARVING

Carving may be performed on the flat ground or in transition.

Carving is when we turn while keeping all four wheels on the ground or wall or ramp.

Carving very much resembles surfing with the way it looks and is done by applying pressure on either your toes or heels to help you turn in a particular direction.

NOTE: Carving in a zigzag formation can be used as a form of pumping on flat ground.

Weekly Planner

week of _____

MONDAY	
TUESDAY	
WEDNESDAY	
THURSDAY	
FRIDAY	
SATURDAY	
SUNDAY	

⊚ GOALS

_____

_____

_____

_____

_____

_____

_____

FEELINGS, SUMMARY, PROGRESS

WEEKLY QUOTES

Grip tape is applied to the top of the board to keep it from being too slippery. Griptape has a sandpaper feel and is meant to provide traction to help you have control of the board.
(See page 8 for a visual)

OLLIES

If you have ever wowed at a skateboarder pulling off stunts mid-air, note that they almost always start off using an Ollie. The Ollie is a technique that enables riders to jump with their boards without using their hands.

Ensure that your rear foot is rested on the tail while your front foot is positioned between the two trucks. The closer that you have your foot to the middle of the board the better it will be. Balance yourself by crouching and bending your knees.

THE JUMP

Once you have a comfortable foot position you can begin.

Because the Ollie is basically jumping, you

Start by blending your knees to jump vertically.

On the way down you should have your weight in the middle of the Board.

Always use the foot that is between the trucks to propel yourself upward (or jump with).

While jumping up, use the foot that is on the tail of the board to press the tail to the ground (this will cause the front end of the board to lift off of the ground).

As the front of the board is lifted off of the ground, slide the side of your front foot up to the nose of the board so that it can make contact with the nose and cause the board to level out

LEVELING OUT

After leveling, you will realize that the board is preparing to come down. Remain focused and continue to keep the board leveled.

LANDING

All four wheels must land at the same time, and your feet must be on their dedicated truck's bolts. Both your knees must be bent to absorb the landing's impact and to stay balanced. Once you start pushing, you can return to your actual position.

Weekly Planner

week of _____

MONDAY

TUESDAY

WEDNESDAY

THURSDAY

FRIDAY

SATURDAY

SUNDAY

◎ GOALS

_____

_____

_____

_____

_____

_____

Wheels help the board move
and hold the bearings
inside them. You get four
wheels in skateboarding.
(See page 8 for a visual)

SHUV IT

The "Shuv It" is a trick that causes the board to spin 180 degrees underneath the skaters feet.

A "Shuv It" or "Pop Shuv It" can turn backside or frontside.

The Difference between a "Shuv It" and a " Pop Shuv It" is that
The "Shuv It" does not necessarily become air born while the "Pop Shuv It" Does

Note: Typicaly a backside "Shuv It" is commonly referred to as a "Shuv It" by default

Setup:
To setup for a "Shuv it" place your front foot on the middle of the board; then put your back foot on the middle of the tail.

Bend your knees then hop vertically like an Ollie. Press down with the foot that is on the tail And move your back foot behind you in a motion that would raise your heel into the air behind you.

(This creates the "Shuv It"motion)

Allow the board to rotate 180 degrees by moving your front foot up and out of the way.

Stop the rotation by catching the board with your front foot first and landing bolts.

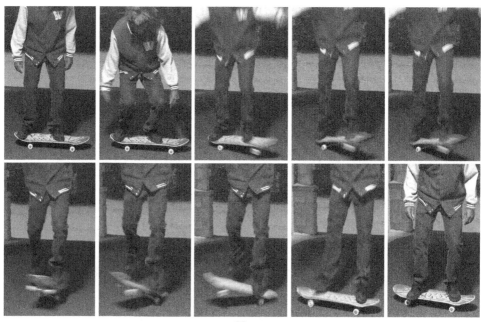

POP SHUVIT

Follow the same instructions for the "Shuv It" and this time jump up vertically.

Press the tail down to the ground like an Ollie and follow through with the "Shuv It" motion with your back foot while sliding your front towards the nose like an Ollie.

Allow the board to rotate under your feet 180 degrees and catch the board with your front foot.

Land bolts and roll away clean.

This pictured shuv is known as a front shuv. The frontside pop shuv it turns in the same direction that a frontside 180 would turn.

We do frontside pop shuvs by pushing our foot that's on the tail or nose when we pop the board forward towards the front of our bodies.

Weekly Planner

week of _____

MONDAY	
TUESDAY	
WEDNESDAY	
THURSDAY	
FRIDAY	
SATURDAY	
SUNDAY	

◎ GOALS

_____

_____

_____

_____

_____

_____

WEEKLY QUOTES

BOLTS:
Bolts keep your trucks
attached to your board.
You get a set of eight bolts.
Most bolts are either
"Allen key" style or
"Phillips head".

Note check your bolts regularly
as they may become loosened
after excessive use

OLLIES

Here you can see Aaron ollieing a gap

NOLLIE

"Nollie" means Nose Ollie. As the name suggests, it entails performing an Ollie off the board's nose.

For this trick, you must ride forward in your normal stance. Your back foot must be positioned in the middle of your board between the trucks, while your front foot's ball must stand at the middle of the nose of the board before you start.

THE JUMP

Having your weight in the middle of the board, jump vertically and press the nose of the board to the ground.

This will cause the tail end of the board to lift off of the ground.

LEVELING OUT

When you are in the air, slide your back foot to the tail and let the board level out. Once you allow your front foot and the nose to rise, the board becomes levelcd.

Now land gracefully.

Weekly Planner

week of _____

MONDAY

TUESDAY

WEDNESDAY

THURSDAY

FRIDAY

SATURDAY

SUNDAY

⊚ GOALS

_____
_____
_____
_____
_____
_____
_____

FEELINGS, SUMMARY, PROGRESS

WEEKLY QUOTES

❝

Every trick has a solution.
It's up to you to unlock it.

❞

Ishod Wair

KICKFLIP

Place your back foot on the tail while you put your front foot in the board's center like an Ollie but with your toes pointed towards the nose at about 45 degrees hanging off of the edge of the heel-side.

Now begin with an Ollie

When your foot gets right behind the front truck bolts proceed to "flick" (pretend you are drawing the uppercase letter U with your foot and use your toes to have the board begin to flip.

The entire movement that you carry out across the nose's corner helps the board flip.

Once you allow your front foot's toes to leave the board, it begins to rotate.

After the board completes a rotation, attempt to catch the board using your back foot then land with both of your feet on the trucks' bolts and continue riding straight.

Mastering Kickflips can take longer than getting used to Ollies.

HEELFLIP

A Heelflip resembles a Kickflip in many ways.

However, the flip is performed in the opposite direction using the heel as opposed to your toes.

Allow your front foot to hang slightly beyond the board's toe edge while your back foot resembles the position it undertakes in an Ollie.

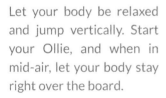

Let your body be relaxed and jump vertically. Start your Ollie, and when in mid-air, let your body stay right over the board.

Flick the board by sliding your front foot to the nose letting the side of your heel hit the corner of the board that is on your front side and follow through.

Lift your legs up to give the board space to turn over.

When you see the grip tape catch the board with your back foot. Bend your knees a when you land so you can endure the impact.

Weekly Planner

week of _____

MONDAY

TUESDAY

WEDNESDAY

THURSDAY

FRIDAY

SATURDAY

SUNDAY

◎ GOALS

_____

_____

_____

_____

_____

_____

_____

Bearings are circular
mechanical wheels that go in
your skateboard wheels and
on your trucks.
There are 8 bearings on a
complete skateboard setup.
(See page 8 for a visual)

BACKSIDE 180

Set your feet in a comfortable Ollie position

Start your Ollie and follow through with rotating your arms and shoulders letting your legs follow.

Wind your arms and shoulders in preparation to turn backside.

Land having turned 180 degrees and look where you are rolling

FRONTSIDE 180

Set your feet in a comfortable Ollie position.

Wind your arms and shoulders in preparation to turn frontside

Start your Ollie and follow through with rotating your arms and shoulders letting your legs follow

Land having turned 180 degrees and look where you are rolling

Weekly Planner

week of _____

MONDAY

TUESDAY

WEDNESDAY

THURSDAY

FRIDAY

SATURDAY

SUNDAY

🎯 GOALS

_____
_____
_____
_____
_____
_____

FEELINGS, SUMMARY, PROGRESS

WEEKLY QUOTES

"

You have to commit; you have to commit to start, you have to commit to land your tricks. Everything is commitment

"

Rachelle Vinberg

DROPIN

Drop In refers to the trick where the skateboarder enters a quarter pipe, bank, pool or bowl right from the top on coping.

1. Position the tail of the board over the coping while your rear foot is on the tail. Place your entire weight on the tail as you put your other foot on the front truck's bolts, applying zero weight.

2. When you begin to drop in, remember to shift your weight to have your weight positioned over the middle of your board. Do not forget to bend your knees and lean forward. Allow your front wheels to contact the ramp as soon as possible.

3. Once you begin rolling, allow your body to stay centered , lower your center of gravity by squatting and refrain from leaning excessively or you may end up falling forward.

Note:
I highly recommend that you start from the bottom and roll up to the coping from the flat bottom of your first drop in ramp

PUMPING

Pumping is how we navigate and control our speed when skating transition.(Ramps, pools, bowls ect...)

When pumping it is good to have a low center of gravity.
A crouched stance will help you keep your balance.

I recommend starting by rolling slowly so you can get comfortable with the transition.

Starting from flat ground approach the transition With your knees bent and you can gradually go higher each time by increasing your speed.

Now the act of pumping is when you push the board through the transition with your feet.

While going up the transition

Slowly begin to stand up and crouch again once you are on the other side of the transition.

On the way back down or when you come back Fakie through the transition crouch when you enter the transition and stand up after you roll away from the transition.

There is a down up down up rhythm that will develop.

Note : SLOWING DOWN.
crouching on the way up a ramp or wall will help slow you down and standing up through transition will also help slow you down

Effectively pumping through transition can help you either maintain speed or speed up

Weekly Planner

week of _____

MONDAY

TUESDAY

WEDNESDAY

THURSDAY

FRIDAY

SATURDAY

SUNDAY

◎ GOALS

_____
_____
_____
_____
_____
_____

FEELINGS, SUMMARY, PROGRESS

WEEKLY QUOTES

Trucks help your board turn and help attach your bearings and wheels to your board.
Trucks are made of a baseplate, kingpin, bushings and washers and a hanger.
(See page 8 for a visual)

KICKTURNS / PIVOTS

Kickturns are performed when we are skating transition.

We typically see Kickturns on Ramps or in pools or bowls.

To do a Kickturn we go up the ramp and then turn around by lifting the front of the board off of the surface and pivoting 180 degrees.

Kickturns can be performed either backside or frontside.

NOTE: Pivots are typically performed on flat ground Yet a pivot and a kickturn is basically the same thing.

MANUAL

A traditional manual is performed when we balance ourselves on two wheels typically the front or back of the board.

To do a manual we put the palm of our back foot on the middle of the tail and keep our front foot in a comfortable place preferably close to the bolts of the front truck.

Shift your weight so that your balance is over the back truck and lift your front foot just enough to getthe front wheels offof the ground.

Now just balance over your back truck and when you are finishe just put your front wheels down.

NOTE: manuals can be performed in all four stances...
Normal, Switch, Nose manny and Fakie manny

Weekly Planner

week of _____

MONDAY	
TUESDAY	
WEDNESDAY	
THURSDAY	
FRIDAY	
SATURDAY	
SUNDAY	

◎ GOALS

_____

_____

_____

_____

_____

_____

FEELINGS, SUMMARY, PROGRESS

WEEKLY QUOTES

Fun Fact: Samarria Brevard became the first African-American female skateboarder to win the Kimberly Diamond Cup.

Weekly Planner

week of _____

MONDAY

TUESDAY

WEDNESDAY

THURSDAY

FRIDAY

SATURDAY

SUNDAY

🎯 GOALS

_____

_____

_____

_____

_____

_____

FEELINGS, SUMMARY, PROGRESS

WEEKLY QUOTES

Fun Fact: Nyjah Huston is currently the highest paid skateboarder with multiple sponsors and several SLS wins.

Weekly Planner

week of _____

MONDAY

TUESDAY

WEDNESDAY

THURSDAY

FRIDAY

SATURDAY

SUNDAY

◎ GOALS

_____

_____

_____

_____

_____

_____

FEELINGS, SUMMARY, PROGRESS

WEEKLY QUOTES

Weekly Planner

week of _____

MONDAY

TUESDAY

WEDNESDAY

THURSDAY

FRIDAY

SATURDAY

SUNDAY

🎯 GOALS

- _____
- _____
- _____
- _____
- _____
- _____

Fun fact: Tony Hawk
invented over 100 vert tricks.

Weekly Planner

week of _____

MONDAY	
TUESDAY	
WEDNESDAY	
THURSDAY	
FRIDAY	
SATURDAY	
SUNDAY	

◎ GOALS

_____

_____

_____

_____

_____

_____

_____

FEELINGS, SUMMARY, PROGRESS

WEEKLY QUOTES

Notable Skating Competitions:
Street League Skateboarding
(SLS), Dew Tour, X-Games,
Mystic Sk8 Cup, The Tampa Pro

Weekly Planner

MONDAY

TUESDAY

WEDNESDAY

THURSDAY

FRIDAY

SATURDAY

SUNDAY

◎ GOALS

_____

_____

_____

_____

_____

_____

FEELINGS, SUMMARY, PROGRESS

WEEKLY QUOTES

Bank: A slanted wall that
can be skated up on to
perform tricks on.
(See page 9 for a visual)

Weekly Planner

week of _____

MONDAY

TUESDAY

WEDNESDAY

THURSDAY

FRIDAY

SATURDAY

SUNDAY

◎ GOALS

_____

_____

_____

_____

_____

_____

_____

FEELINGS, SUMMARY, PROGRESS

WEEKLY QUOTES

Weekly Planner

week of _____

MONDAY	
TUESDAY	
WEDNESDAY	
THURSDAY	
FRIDAY	
SATURDAY	
SUNDAY	

◎ GOALS

_____

_____

_____

_____

_____

_____

FEELINGS, SUMMARY, PROGRESS

WEEKLY QUOTES

Fun fact: Rodney Mullen is known as the Godfather of street skating and invented tricks such as the kickflip, impossible, and the 360-flip.

Weekly Planner

week of _____

MONDAY

TUESDAY

WEDNESDAY

THURSDAY

FRIDAY

SATURDAY

SUNDAY

◎ GOALS

_____
_____
_____
_____
_____
_____
_____

Remember:
Don't skate on injuries!

Weekly Planner

week of _____

MONDAY	
TUESDAY	
WEDNESDAY	
THURSDAY	
FRIDAY	
SATURDAY	
SUNDAY	

⊚ GOALS

_____
_____
_____
_____
_____
_____
_____

FEELINGS, SUMMARY, PROGRESS

WEEKLY QUOTES

Snake: Someone who cuts
other skaters off and generally
doesn't wait for their turn.

Weekly Planner

week of _____

MONDAY

TUESDAY

WEDNESDAY

THURSDAY

FRIDAY

SATURDAY

SUNDAY

⊚ GOALS

- _____
- _____
- _____
- _____
- _____
- _____

WEEKLY QUOTES

Fun fact: Grip tape air bubbles?
Just poke a hole in it and
smooth it out.

Weekly Planner

week of _____

MONDAY

TUESDAY

WEDNESDAY

THURSDAY

FRIDAY

SATURDAY

SUNDAY

⊚ GOALS

_____

_____

_____

_____

_____

_____

_____

FEELINGS, SUMMARY, PROGRESS

WEEKLY QUOTES

Remember: Keep your skate
area debris- free when possible.
Debris includes but is not
limited to trash, pebbles,
and glass.

Weekly Planner

week of _____

MONDAY	
TUESDAY	
WEDNESDAY	
THURSDAY	
FRIDAY	
SATURDAY	
SUNDAY	

◎ GOALS

_____

_____

_____

_____

_____

_____

_____

FEELINGS, SUMMARY, PROGRESS

WEEKLY QUOTES

Fun Fact: Sky Brown, age 11, is the first female to land a frontside 540 at the 2019 Summer X-Games.

Weekly Planner

week of _____

MONDAY

TUESDAY

WEDNESDAY

THURSDAY

FRIDAY

SATURDAY

SUNDAY

🎯 GOALS

_____
_____
_____
_____
_____
_____
_____

FEELINGS, SUMMARY, PROGRESS

WEEKLY QUOTES

"

Skateboarding is a lifestyle. If I wasn't a professional skateboarder, I'd be skating every day.

"

Ryan Sheckler

Weekly Planner

week of _____

MONDAY

TUESDAY

WEDNESDAY

THURSDAY

FRIDAY

SATURDAY

SUNDAY

◎ GOALS

_____

_____

_____

_____

_____

_____

WEEKLY QUOTES

"

I embrace the "Better Than Yesterday" mindset everyday. It's what I live by... I'm always in search of how I can better myself as a person, in the gym and on my skateboard.
I love learning more each day.

"

Neen Williams

TRICK LIST

FLIPS & POP SHUV ITS

Flip tricks and pop shuvits are essentially Ollies. The primary difference is that in mid-air, the board is either flipped or spun.

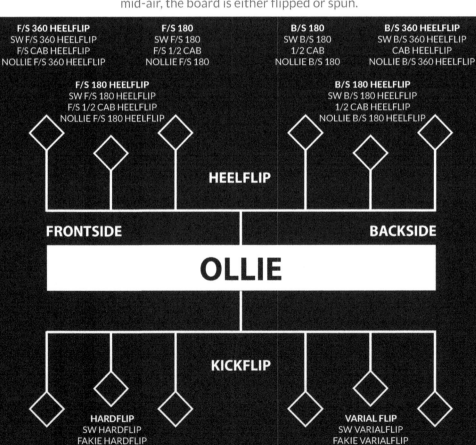

F/S 360 HEELFLIP
SW F/S 360 HEELFLIP
F/S CAB HEELFLIP
NOLLIE F/S 360 HEELFLIP

F/S 180
SW F/S 180
F/S 1/2 CAB
NOLLIE F/S 180

B/S 180
SW B/S 180
1/2 CAB
NOLLIE B/S 180

B/S 360 HEELFLIP
SW B/S 360 HEELFLIP
CAB HEELFLIP
NOLLIE B/S 360 HEELFLIP

F/S 180 HEELFLIP
SW F/S 180 HEELFLIP
F/S 1/2 CAB HEELFLIP
NOLLIE F/S 180 HEELFLIP

B/S 180 HEELFLIP
SW B/S 180 HEELFLIP
1/2 CAB HEELFLIP
NOLLIE B/S 180 HEELFLIP

HEELFLIP

FRONTSIDE

BACKSIDE

OLLIE

KICKFLIP

HARDFLIP
SW HARDFLIP
FAKIE HARDFLIP
NOLLIE VARIAL KICKFLIP

VARIAL FLIP
SW VARIALFLIP
FAKIE VARIALFLIP
NOLLIE HARDFLIP

360 HARDFLIP
SW 360 HARDFLIP
FAKIE 360 HARDFLIP
NOLLIE 360 FLIP

F/S SHUV-IT
SW F/S SHUV-IT
FAKIE F/S SHUV-IT
NOLLIE F/S SHUV-IT

B/S SHUV-IT
SW F/S SHUV-IT
FAKIE F/S SHUV-IT
NOLLIE F/S SHUV-IT

360 HARDFLIP
SW 360 HARDFLIP
FAKIE 360 HARDFLIP
NOLLIE 360 FLIP

TRICK CHECK LIST

BASICS

- [ ] Pushing
- [ ] Carving
- [ ] Kickturns
- [ ] Tic-tacs

STREET

- [ ] Ollie
- [ ] Front side 180
- [ ] Back side 180
- [ ] Shuvit
- [ ] Pop Shuvit
- [ ] No Comply
- [ ] Boneless
- [ ] Manual
- [ ] Fakie Shuvit

TRANSITION

- [ ] Rock to Fakie
- [ ] Tail Stall
- [ ] Rock and Roll
- [ ] Axle Stall
- [ ] Fakie rock and roll
- [ ] 360 rock and roll
- [ ] 50-50 Grinds
- [ ] Nose Stall
- [ ] Revert

FLIP TRICKS

- [ ] Kickflip
- [ ] Heelflip
- [ ] Varial kickflip
- [ ] BS 180 Flip

GRINDS

- [ ] Slappy Grind
- [ ] BS Boardslide
- [ ] FS 50-50
- [ ] BS 50-50

BASICS

STREET

TRANSITION

FLIPS

SLIDES/GRINDS

BONUS FUN

SHRED O TOUR
Quarantine BINGO

learned a new trick on the carpet	rode around town with mask on	joined a quarantine skate challenge on IG	tried to visit a skatepark but got locked out	watched at least 10 hours of skate clips
upgraded your setup	uploaded a skate clip on Tiktok	grinded or stalled on the furnish	finger boarded	created a DIY spot in their house or backyard
did flip tricks w/o trucks and wheels on	cleaned your bearings	FREE	visited at least 3 skate parks/spots during Covid	played Tony Hawk video games
kickflipped in pajamas	had the whole skatepark to yourself	skated in the house barefooted or with socks on	freestyled on the carpet	someone got mad at you for skating in the house
got kicked out of the skatepark	parking lot or sidewalk sesh w/ homies	have not touched your board at all	learned at least 4 new tricks/ combos	snapped your board

What is your worst injury from skating?

Would you rather scrape your knees or get bruises?

any stitches?

How many times have you sprained your ankkle?

bloody head?

anything else?

broken bones?

SHRED O TOUR
Cyber Skateboarding Tournament Champions

SkateLaboratory Experiment
July 2020

Sam Hall

PHOTO: TOM BROOKER

OG TRICKS
August 2020

Riley Pascale

SPOOKTACULAR
October 2020

JOE WARNER

Shred Harder Tournament
October 2020

COVERT

Michael Hall

FROZONE
February 2021

RONNIE FABRO

Special Shoutout to these amazing local companies and friends! Thank you to everyone -- beta testers, skateboarders, Finacurk, the Pascale Boys, sponsors and voters who have contributed into making this mobile app awesome!

Join the Flock

SHRED O TOUR

YOUR LOCAL SKATE SHOP

IT IS SO IMPORTANT TO SUPPORT YOUR LOCAL SHOP, WHEN YOU SHOP LOCAL YOU OFTEN:

- Help the survival of skate shops, whichoften don't compete well against larger corporations

- Help to pay employee wages

- Help reinvest in the community because a lot of times shops host fun events, competitions, and demos

- Find an awesome community of other skaters!

CAN'T SUPPORT YOUR LOCAL SKATE SHOP?

Consider buying from Bamboo, a socially responsible skate company. They say for every skateboard you buy, a tree will be planted!

ENTER THIS LINK BELOW
bit.ly/39akgrU125

Special shout out to Shrimptown Skate Shop IG @shrimptownskateshop

CREDIT

PHOTOGRAPHY CREDITS

HoneyShred Baltimore IG @HoneyShred Page 4

Demi Harper with Lydia Embry Photography IG @whatlydiaisdoing Page 4

Aaron Davis IG @Finacurk Page 12

Pia Saclauso owner of Radgals DMV IG @Radgals.dmv Page 13

Maddie Hazlett IG @maddie.hazlett Page 16

Dominus IG @beingsvpreme Page 49

Imoh Ekasi-Otu IG @sk8bdhomi Page 81

Amanda Finnegan IG @PandaCinnamon Page 81

Mia IG@boobsonboards Page 81

Jess Knot Photography IG @jessknottphotography Page 81

Shred.o.tour-Cyber Skate Tournaments IG @shred.o.tour Page 82

Author picture taken by Rachel Keatts IG @mosaicphotographs

OTHER CREDITS

"About Rodney Mullen." Rodney Mullen. https://rodneymullen.com/about

Doug Murray. "The 20 Wealthiest Skateboarders in the World – 2017 Edition. Slice."

August 10, 2017, https://www.slice.ca/money/photos/wealthiest-skateboarders-in-theworld-2017/#!Nyjah-Huston_Wealthiest-Skateboarders_

D'Arcy Maine. "Tony Hawk calls Sky Brown 'a unicorn' on a skateboard." ESPN. Jul

1, 2020, https://www.espn.com/olympics/story/_/id/29364764/tony-hawk-calls-skybrown-unicorn-skateboard

"Invented By Tony Hawk." The Berrics. July 23, 2019,

https://theberrics.com/invented-by-tony-hawk

"Ishod Wair Trick Detective." Thrasher Magazine. 19 July 2018,

www.thrashermagazine.com/articles/ishod-wair-trick-detective/

PixaHombre. "Skateboard Skating Sports Free Photo." Needpix.com,

https://www.needpix.com/photo/848502/skateboard-skating-sports

Thomas, Amara. "Make Skating Radical Again." Fader.

www.thefader.com/2016/09/21/brujas-skate-kitchen-lil-nice-girl-skatinginterview

Neen Williams. Ten Thousand. www.tenthousand.cc/blogs/team/athlete-neenwilliams

Jenisha Watts. "Meet the 'Serena Williams of skateboarding,' Samarria Brevard."

ESPN. Jun 2, 2016, https://www.espn.com/espnw/sports/story/_/id/15889445/meetserena- williams-skateboarding-samarria-brevard

About The Author

My name is Yuri Cruz better known as The Gnarly Nurse and I'm a multi-passionate nurse and recreational skateboarder. I love using my creativity, knowledge, and out-of-the box thinking to help others reach their goals. This is dedicated to the dreamers and to all the beautiful and successful people reading this right now. I hope this book inspires you and is helpful to you during your skateboarding journey!

Made in the USA
Middletown, DE
06 August 2021